In Level 0, **Step 6** build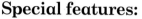 previous steps and introduces new sounds and their letters:

ch   **sh**   **th**   **th**   **ng**
                   (soft)   (hard)

Special features:

Phonically decodable text builds reading confidence

Short sentences with simple language

The netting has a gap in it. Chad tells his Dad that a fox can get in.

Dad nods.

A fox will get in the chicken shed unless we fix it.

8

9

Repetition of sounds in different words

Story Words

Can you match these words to the pictures?

Chad
Dad
chickens
shed
netting
jacket

16

Tricky Words

These tricky words are in the story you have just read. They cannot be sounded out. Can you memorize them and read them super fast?

to   into
the   all
he

17

Summary page to reinforce learning

Practice of words that cannot be sounded out

Educational consultant: Geraldine Taylor

Phonics and Book Banding Consultant: Kate Ruttle

LADYBIRD BOOKS

UK | USA | Canada | Ireland | Australia
India | New Zealand | South Africa

Ladybird Books is part of the Penguin Random House group of companies
whose addresses can be found at global.penguinrandomhouse.com.

www.penguin.co.uk   www.puffin.co.uk   www.ladybird.co.uk

First edition published 2020
001

Printed in China

A CIP catalogue record for this book is available from the British Library

ISBN: 978-0-241-40509-3

All correspondence to
Ladybird Books
Penguin Random House Children's
80 Strand, London WC2R 0RL

Chad and his Dad

Written by Alison Hawes
Illustrated by Hannah Wood

Chad picks up the eggs
in the shed.

He can not get them all
in the box.

The extra egg is in
Dad's pocket.

The netting has a gap in it. Chad tells his Dad that a fox can get in.

A fox will get in the chicken shed unless we fix it.

Dad nods.

Dad hangs up his jacket.
Then he cuts the thick
netting.

Dad tacks the netting
to the shed. Bang!
Bash! Bang!

At six, the chickens dash
into the chicken shed.

Chad shuts them in.

It is a fox. He tugs at the netting. He can not get the chickens . . .

. . . but he can get the egg in Dad's jacket!

Story Words

Can you match these words to the pictures?

Chad

Dad

chickens

shed

netting

jacket

Tricky Words

These tricky words are in the story you have just read. They cannot be sounded out. Can you memorize them and read them super fast?

to   into

the   all

he

Banana Muffins

Written by Alison Hawes
Illustrated by Hannah Wood

Chad has a dish of muffin mix. He adds an egg to the mix.

21

Chad adds the banana to the dish.

I can mash the banana.

Then Chad fills the muffin
tin with the mix.

Dad and Chad finish up.
Then they relax.

Dad nods off. Chad checks on the muffins. He yells at Dad.

Chad cuts the tops off
the muffins.

Chad chops up the bananas.
He puts the jam and banana
on top of the muffins.

Chad and Dad tuck into
the muffins.

Yum!

Story Words

Can you match these words
to the pictures?

jam

egg

muffin

egg shell

dish

banana